Elrose Hunter and Eira Reeves

CW00859093

David
THE GIANT KILLER

Copyright © Elrose Hunter 2004
First published 2004
Reprinted 2008, 2009

ISBN 978 1 84427 076 7

Scripture Union, 207–209 Queensway, Bletchley, Milton Keynes, MK2 2EB, England
Email:info@scriptureunion.org.uk
Website:www.scriptureunion.org.uk

Scripture Union Australia
Locked Bag 2, Central Coast Business Centre, NSW 2252, Australia
Website:www.scriptureunion.org.au

Scripture Union USA
PO Box 987, Valley Forge, PA 19482, USA
Website:www.scriptureunion.org

The right of Elrose Hunter to be identified as author of this work has been asserted by her in accordance with the Copyright, Designs and Patents Act 1988.

The right of Eira Reeves to be identified as illustrator of this work has been asserted by her in accordance with the Copyright, Designs and Patents Act 1988.

Scripture quotations are from the Contemporary English Version published by Harper Collins Publishers, copyright © 1991, 1992, 1995 American Bible Society.

British Library Cataloguing-in-Publication Data.
A catalogue record of this book is available from the British Library.

Printed and bound in Singapore by Tien Wah Press Ltd.

Cover design:fourninezerodesign

Scripture Union is an international Christian charity working with churches in more than 130 countries, providing resources to bring the good news about Jesus Christ to children, young people and families and to encourage them to develop spiritually through the Bible and prayer.

As well as our network of volunteers, staff and associates who run holidays, church-based events and school Christian groups, we produce a wide range of publications and support those who use our resources through training programmes.

David lived long ago in the land of Israel. He was a shepherd boy and looked after his father's sheep on the hills around Bethlehem. He had seven older brothers. They didn't think much of David. "Huh! You're only a shepherd. What do you know about anything?" they said.

Colour the drawing of David the shepherd and add more sheep to the picture.

Sometimes wild animals attacked the sheep and David had to defend them. One day he heard a lamb bleating in fear. David saw that a bear had sneaked up and was about to grab the lamb. He ran at the bear and hit it with his club. The lamb was saved and this bear would never attack sheep again!

Join the dots to discover another animal that attacked David's sheep one day.

One day a servant came running to fetch David from the fields. David arrived home hot and breathless. God's messenger, Samuel, was visiting and all David's brothers were lined up in front of him. "God has a special job for you," Samuel told David. He poured oil over David's head as a sign that God had chosen him to be king one day.

Write the first letter of the word for each picture to discover why David was chosen to be king instead of any of his brothers.

CODE

🐦 = G

🌳 = D

☀ = t

_avid _rusted _od.

David loved to play the harp and write songs while he looked after the sheep. Here is one of David's songs:

You, <u>Lord</u>, are my <u>shepherd</u>.

I will never be in need.

You let me <u>rest</u> in fields of green <u>grass</u>.

You <u>lead</u> me to streams of peaceful <u>water</u>.

Find the underlined words of the song in the wordsearch. Look across and down. Circle the words when you find them.

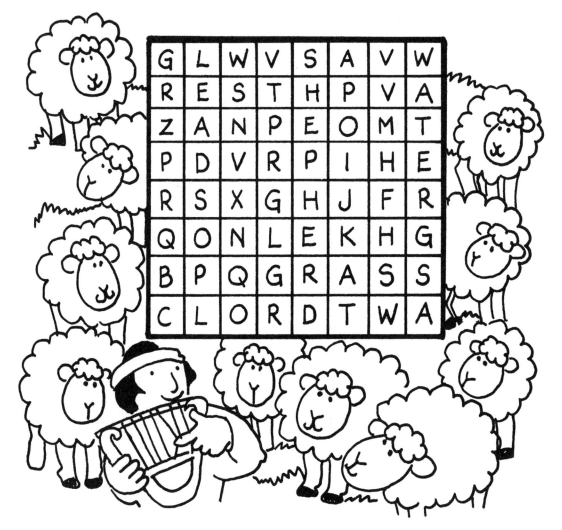

G	L	W	V	S	A	V	W
R	E	S	T	H	P	V	A
Z	A	N	P	E	O	M	T
P	D	V	R	P	I	H	E
R	S	X	G	H	J	F	R
Q	O	N	L	E	K	H	G
B	P	Q	G	R	A	S	S
C	L	O	R	D	T	W	A

King Saul heard about David, the shepherd boy who played the harp. "Send for David," he said to his servants one day when he was feeling miserable. So David came and played his harp and sang his songs and King Saul felt much better.

Look at the picture of David playing music to King Saul and find six things that would not have been there in David's time.

David's elder brothers were in King Saul's army, fighting the Philistines. One day, David's father gave him a parcel of food to take to his brothers. "Find out how they are getting on," he said. When David arrived, he found the soldiers very frightened because of a challenge from a giant in the Philistine army.

Write the first letter of the word for each picture in the centre of the picture wheel to discover the name of the giant.

The giant Goliath was a terrifying sight! He was nearly three metres tall and wore heavy bronze armour. "I dare you to pick someone to fight me!" Goliath shouted. "If he wins, we will all be your slaves. If I win, you will all be our slaves."

Copying square by square, use the grid to draw the other half of the giant.

David went to see King Saul. He said, "Your Majesty, I will fight this giant." "You're just a boy. How could you fight him?" answered Saul. Then David told him about the lion and the bear that he had killed while looking after his sheep. "God helped me then and he will help me now," David said.

Unjumble the words to find out what Saul said to David next and colour in the picture.

_____ , _____   _____   _____

_____   _____ .

"Take my armour if you're going to fight Goliath," said King Saul. So David tried on the helmet and the heavy suit of armour. But he could hardly move in it! "I can't fight in this," David said, and he took it all off again. Then he walked over to a stream and put something into his shepherd's bag.

Use the code in the box to discover what David put into his bag.

___	___	___	___		
A3	B1	C3	D1		

___	___	___	___	___	___
A2	D3	B2	B2	B4	C1

___	___	___	___	___	___
A2	B4	B2	A1	D1	A2

	1	2	3	4
A	n	s	f	p
B	i	o	z	t
C	h	k	v	b
D	e	r	m	g

Goliath roared with laughter when he saw David coming with his shepherd's stick in his hand. "What's that stick for? Do you think I'm a dog?" he jeered and cursed David.

"You have insulted God, but he will help me defeat you," David answered. And with that, he put a stone into his catapult and hurled it at Goliath. It hit his forehead and the giant fell forward on his face. Then David lifted the giant's sword and cut off his head.

Draw a line to connect the two shields which are exactly the same and colour them in.

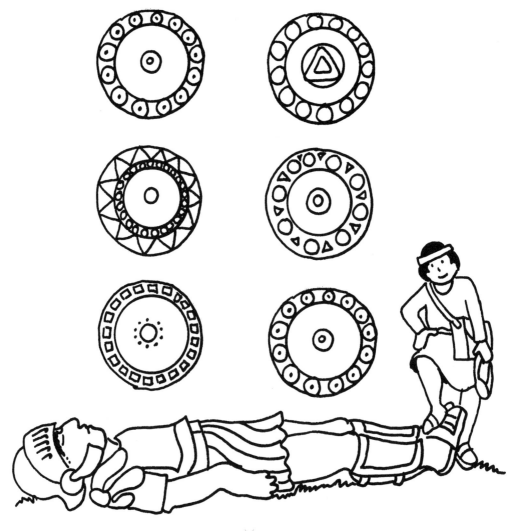

When the Philistine soldiers saw that Goliath was dead, they turned and ran away. The Israelite soldiers chased them back to their own land. David was a hero! People came out of the towns to cheer him. Women danced in the streets and sang a song about him.

Fill in the missing letters in the word to complete the song the women sang:

Saul has killed th _____ _____ s _____ nds

but David t _____ ns of th _____ _____ s _____ nds

Choose from a,e,o,u.

King Saul did not like the song praising David. He was jealous because David was so popular. "They might even want to make him king!" he said. So the next time David played his harp for the king, Saul threw a spear at him. It missed him but David knew he was in danger.

Find five differences between the two pictures.

David had learned to trust God with his life. Here is part of the song he wrote about God looking after him.

I may <u>walk</u> through valleys

As <u>dark</u> as death, but I won't be <u>afraid</u>.

You are with me,

and your shepherd's <u>rod</u> makes me feel <u>safe</u>.

Find the underlined words of the song in the wordsearch. Look across, down and diagonally. Circle the words when you find them.

B	D	E	Z	Q	R	O	D
R	A	P	J	F	L	S	W
P	R	E	Z	J	P	T	A
N	K	Q	V	C	R	A	F
S	N	I	W	A	L	K	R
X	A	D	G	H	J	D	A
V	S	F	R	Y	N	L	I
H	S	E	E	R	F	J	D

King Saul had a son called Jonathan who became a very good friend of David. When Jonathan found out that Saul planned to kill David, he tried to persuade his father not to do it. "Remember how David risked his life when he killed Goliath," Jonathan said. At first Saul agreed, but not for long. Soon David was in danger again and Jonathan too.

Help David escape through the palace maze away from the angry king.

Jonathan worked out a secret way to warn David when King Saul was planning to kill him. David hid in a field and Jonathan came nearby with his bow and arrows. He brought a young boy with him to collect the arrows. When Jonathan shot an arrow beyond the boy, he shouted, "Hurry! The arrow is further away."

Unjumble the words to find out what Jonathan meant.

_____ _____! _____ _____

_____ _____.

David married Saul's daughter, Michal. Saul sent men to watch the house and trap David. Michal warned him, "You've got to run away from here tonight!" So she let David down from a back window and he escaped in the dark. Then she planned how to trick the men next day.

Look at the BEFORE and AFTER pictures to discover what Michal did to make it seem as if David was still there. What other differences can you see?

BEFORE   AFTER

Next day the king's men came to the door to fetch David. "David is ill in bed," Michal told them. When they told Saul, he shouted, "Bring him here in his bed!" So the men went back to the house and found they had been tricked. Saul was furious!

Put the pictures in the right order for the story.
Write the numbers 1 to 4 in the boxes.

David knew that he had to hide from King Saul. A group of his loyal friends joined him and they lived in caves in the hills. One day, David's friend Jonathan came to see him. Jonathan wanted to cheer David up and told him he would always be his friend.

Use the code to discover what else Jonathan told David.

Saul found out where David was hiding and brought his best soldiers to capture him. They camped overnight and David took one of his men right into the camp to where Saul was sleeping. The man wanted to kill Saul but David said, "No! We must leave that to God." So they crept away, taking two things as proof that they had been there.

Unscramble the words to discover what David took away.

pasre   tewar rja

_____   _____   _____

David went to a safe distance away from the camp before he shouted to wake up Saul's bodyguard. "Where is the king's spear and water jar?" he called. "You should protect the king better!" Saul realised that David had spared his life. "I have been a fool," he said and gave up chasing David.

Start with the letter a and cross out every other letter to discover what creatures David said he felt like, when he was being chased by King Saul.

axfrljepaqaowyiglvdkbsiwrzd

After King Saul was killed in a battle with the Philistines, David became king. He ruled for forty years and he made Jerusalem the capital city of his kingdom. The king of Tyre sent David cedar logs and carpenters and stone masons to build a palace. David thanked God for keeping him safe and making him king of Israel.

Look at the building site and find five silly things in it.

The warlike Philistines sent an army to capture David. So he asked God, "Shall I attack them? Will you give me the victory?"

Unscramble the words to see what God said to David and colour in the picture.

,seY kcatta!

_____   _____

David knew that something was missing in Jerusalem. The special Covenant Box, containing the laws God gave to Moses, should be there. So he ordered the priests to fetch it. David and his men formed a great procession. All the people came out to welcome the Box and to sing and praise God. David danced along with the others.

Can you match the names to the instruments?

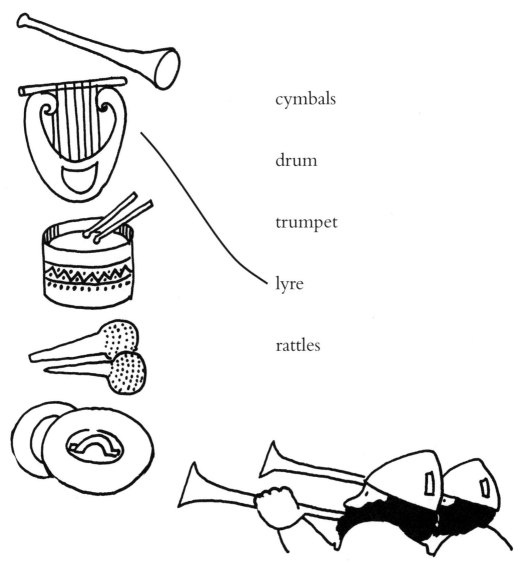

cymbals

drum

trumpet

lyre

rattles

David was very sad when his friend Jonathan was killed in battle. He asked his servants whether any of Jonathan's family was still alive. "Yes," they said, "he has a lame son." David told them to fetch Mephibosheth. When he arrived, he looked frightened. "Don't be afraid," David said gently. "I want to help you. You can live here from now on." Mephibosheth was amazed that the king was so kind to him.

Unscramble the words in the speech bubble to discover why David was kind to Mephibosheth.

_____ _____ ____ __ _____ _____.

David had not finished fighting battles when he became king. There were wars against the Philistines, the Syrians and other nations who wanted to snatch the kingdom from David. But God helped David to defeat them all. David wrote a song of praise to God:

Finish the other half of the drawing of the fortress and colour it in.

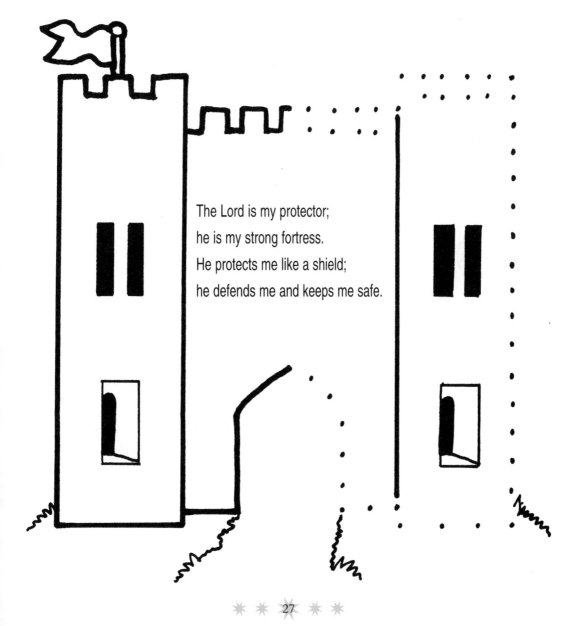

The Lord is my protector;
he is my strong fortress.
He protects me like a shield;
he defends me and keeps me safe.

"I feel bad because I live in a fine palace but God's Covenant Box lives in a tent," David said to Nathan, one of God's messengers. "I would like to build a temple for it." God spoke to Nathan. "Tell David that he is not the one to build a temple for me. After he dies, his son will build a great temple for me."

Use the letters on the bricks to spell the name of David's son who would build the temple.

___ ___ ___ ___ ___ ___ ___

God promised David that his kingdom would last forever. Although Israel disobeyed God and God allowed their enemies to defeat them for a time, he never forgot his promise to David. Hundreds of years later one of David's descendants was born in Bethlehem, David's home town. His name was Jesus.

Complete the words of this Christmas carol about David's descendant.

Once in royal D __ __ __ __ ' __ city

Stood a lowly c __ __ __ __ __ shed,

Where a mother laid her b __ __ __

In a m __ __ __ __ __ for his bed,

M __ __ __ was that mother mild,

J __ __ __ __ Christ her little child.

ANSWERS

page 5	David trusted God
page 7	television, headphones, books, lamp, toy car, computer.
page 8	Goliath
page 10	Go, and the Lord be with you.
page 11	five smooth stones
page 13	thousands, tens, thousands
page 17	Run away! God be with you.
page 20	You will be king and I will be next to you
page 21	spear, water jar
page 22	a flea; a wild bird
page 23	teapot, teddy bear, aeroplane, boots, bobble hat
page 24	Yes, attack!
page 26	Your father was my truest friend.
page 28	Solomon
page 29	David's, cattle, baby, manger, Mary, Jesus

There are 3 more puzzle books in this series to collect.
Look out for them!

978 1 84427 078 1
£2.50

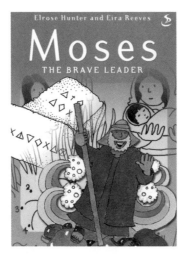

978 1 84427 075 0
£2.50

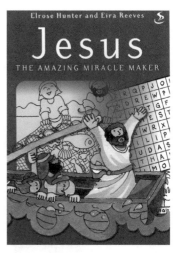

978 1 84427 077 4
£2.50

Look out for great puzzle books about Abraham, Joseph, Daniel and Peter!

You can buy all of these books at Christian bookshops,
online at www.scriptureunion.org.uk/publishing
or call Mail Order direct: 0845 0706 006

For more fun look out for these *Crazy Stories* by Alexander Brown.

Anthony Greenfinger is a farmer. He loves his chickens, his cows and the fleas but he longs for one more thing: apples! He sets out to plant apple trees but things don't go quite according to plan when he makes a very silly mistake!

ISBN 978 1 84427 262 4
£3.99

ISBN 978 1 84427 337 9
£3.99

ISBN 978 1 84427 338 6
£3.99

ISBN 978 1 84427 263 1
£3.99

Order a copy at your local Christian bookshop or from:
Scripture Union Mail Order, PO Box 5148, Milton Keynes MKO, MK2 2YX.
Tel: 0845 0706006 www.scriptureunion.org.uk